What Shall We Do When We All Go Out?

A Traditional Song, Illustrated by

Shari Halpern

HOUGHTON MIFFLIN COMPANY

BOSTON

ATLANTA   DALLAS   GENEVA, ILLINOIS   PALO ALTO   PRINCETON

FOR JUDY SUE

**What shall we do when we all go out,
all go out, all go out?**

What shall we do when we all go out,
When we all go out to play?

We will ride our three-wheel bikes,
three-wheel bikes, three-wheel bikes.
We will ride our three-wheel bikes
When we all go out to play!

8

We will seesaw up and down,
up and down, up and down.
We will seesaw up and down
When we all go out to play!

We will run and somersault,
somersault, somersault.
We will run and somersault
When we all go out to play!

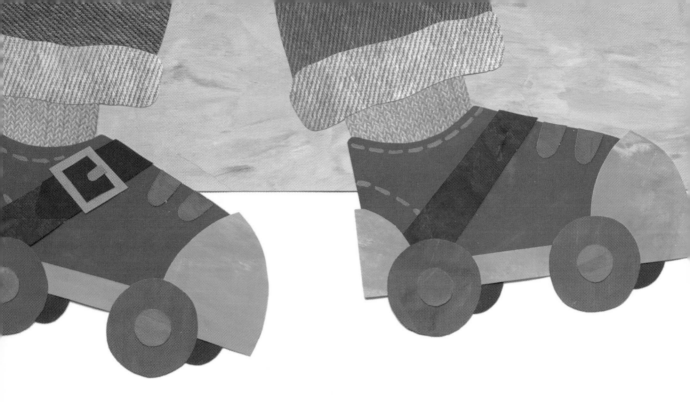

We will wear our roller skates,
roller skates, roller skates.
We will wear our roller skates
When we all go out to play!

Then we'll sit and eat our lunch,
eat our lunch, eat our lunch.
Then we'll sit and eat our lunch
In the middle of the day!

What shall we do in the afternoon,
afternoon, afternoon?
What shall we do in the afternoon
After we've had lunch?

We will stop to feed the ducks,
feed the ducks, feed the ducks.
We will stop to feed the ducks
After we've had lunch!

20

We will fly our long-tailed kites,
long-tailed kites, long-tailed kites.
We will fly our long-tailed kites
After we've had lunch!

We will climb a great big tree,
a great big tree, a great big tree.
We will climb a great big tree
When we all go back to play!

We will all play hide-and-seek,
hide-and seek, hide-and-seek.
We will all play hide-and-seek
till it's time for us to go!

What shall we do when we all go in,
all go in, all go in?
What shall we do when we all go in,
When we all go in from play?

We will sit and sip our soup,
sip our soup, sip our soup.
We will sit and sip our soup
And think about TOMORROW!